ISLAND OF THE BLUE DOLPHINS

by
Scott O'Dell

Student Packet

Written by
Gloria Levine, M.A.

Contains masters for:

2	Prereading Activities
8	Vocabulary Activities
1	Study Guide
1	Geography Activity
3	Critical Thinking Activities
2	Literary Analysis Activities
1	Research Project
4	Writing Activities
1	Review Crossword
2	Comprehension Quizzes (Honors and Average)
2	Unit Exams (Honors and Average)

PLUS Detailed Answer Key

Note

The text used to prepare this guide was the Laurel Leaf Historical Fiction softcover published by Dell Publishing, ©1960 by Scott O'Dell.

Please note: Please assess the appropriateness of this book for the age level and maturity of your students prior to reading and discussing it with your class.

1-56137-489-X

To order, contact your local school supply store, or—

Novel Units, Inc.
P.O. Box 97
Bulverde, TX 78163-0097

Web site: www.educyberstor.com

Name_____

Anticipation Guide

Directions: Rate each of the following statements before you read the novel (1 means you agree completely or very much—6 means you don't agree at all). Compare your ratings with a partner's, and discuss why you chose the particular ratings you did. (After you have completed the novel, rate the statements again and discuss with your partner whether any of the ratings changed.)

1— — — -2— — — -3— — — -4 — — — -5— — — -6

agree   *strongly*

strongly   *disagree*

_____ Certain jobs should be men's work and other jobs should be women's work.

_____ The ocean and its creatures should belong to everyone.

_____ If you're being cheated, you should fight back.

_____ Living all alone would be a terrible thing.

_____ You should follow the rules set by the adults in your community.

_____ Revenge is sweet.

_____ Boys are better than girls at "roughing it" in nature.

_____ Time passes more slowly when you're lonely or bored.

_____ Killing animals is wrong.

_____ It's not good to make pets of wild animals.

_____ I'd rather live today—with modern conveniences—than in the past, as a hunter and gatherer.

_____ Knowing whom to trust is hard.

_____ Patience is one of the most important qualities to have.

_____ Necessity is the mother of invention.

_____ You can control your fears if you try hard enough.

_____ When you see a problem that needs to be solved, it's better to take risks and try to solve it than to play safe.

Directions: Suppose you found yourself alone on an island in the Pacific Ocean. You face all of the following problems—and more. Rank them in order of importance to you, with "1" being the problem you would need to solve first.

_____ hunger

_____ thirst

_____ loneliness

_____ no cooking utensils

_____ no fire

_____ danger from wild dogs

_____ boredom

_____ no weapons

_____ no way to get off the island

_____ no way to communicate with your family

_____ need to be visible to rescuers

_____ need to remain hidden if enemies come

In a small-group discussion, predict how a girl of 12 might solve these problems. As you read the book, watch for the order in which Karana tackles these problem and the methods she uses to solve them.

Study Questions

Write a brief answer to each study question as you read the novel at home or in class. Use the questions for review before group discussions and before your final exam.

Chapters 1-4:
1. Who is telling the story? How do you imagine her? What is she like?
2. When and where did the story take place?
3. Who is on the ship? Why has it come?
4. Who are Ulape and Ramo?
5. Who is Chief Chowig? Why is Karana surprised that he gives his name to the Aleut stranger?
6. What happened the last time Aleuts came to hunt?
7. How did the island get its name?
8. What do Karana's people refuse to share with the Aleuts? Do you think they should share?
9. What agreement have Chief Chowig and Captain Orlov reached? How long do the Aleuts stay?
10. What happens when the Aleuts break their agreement?

Chapters 5-8:
1. How many of the islanders do the Aleuts kill? How many men remain?
2. Who is Kimki?
3. How do the roles of women change after so many men die? How do the men feel about that?
4. How can you tell that the people were depressed? Why?
5. Where does Kimki go? Is he successful?
6. What does Karana put in the baskets she decides to take on the ship?
7. Why can't the ship wait for Ramo?
8. Why does Karana jump off the ship? Would you have done that?
9. How does Ramo die? How does Karana plan to get revenge?

Chapters 9-11:
1. Why does Karana decide never to live in the village again? What happens to the houses there?
2. Once the village is gone, what does Karana do about shelter?
3. Why does Karana need weapons? Why doesn't she make them, at first?

---

4. What does Karana hope to find in the chest left by the Aleuts? What is in the chest? How can you tell that the Aleuts were planning to deceive Karana's people?
5. What does Karana finally use to make weapons?
6. What does Karana eat?
7. How does Karana feel when winter comes? Why?
8. Why does Karana set out in a canoe? Why does she return?
9. Where does Karana decide to build a house? How?

Chapters 12-15:

1. What does Karana use the whale bones for? What else might she have tried using?
2. What was the legend about Tumaiyowit and Mukat?
3. How does Karana make utensils?
4. How does Karana cook seeds and roots?
5. What does Karana use the bodies of the little dried fish for?
6. Why does Karana want to kill a sea elephant?
7. How does Karana hurt her leg?
8. Why doesn't Karana kill the big gray dog? What does she do instead?
9. How does Karana get what she needs for her spear points?
10. What does Karana name the dog? Why?

Chapters 16-19:

1. How and why does Karana work on the canoe?
2. Why does Karana consider the cave a "great discovery"?
3. What does Karana plan to catch in the water with the spear? Why?
4. Why does Rontu leave Karana? What happens to him and to the pack?
5. What two "new friends" does Karana make? How?
6. Describe the clothes Karana makes for those times when she feels like being "dressed up."
7. What happens when Karana fights the devilfish? Why doesn't she try to spear the two other devilfish she sees later that summer?

Chapters 20-23:

1. How does Karana protect the abalone meat from the birds?
2. Why does Karana kill the ten cormorants?
3. What does Karana find in Black Cave? How does that make her feel?

4. About how old is Karana when the Aleuts come again? What does she do when she sees them arrive?
5. Why is Karana more afraid of the girl than of the men?
6. How does the Aleut girl treat Karana? How does Karana feel toward her, at first?
7. What present does the girl leave for Karana?
8. What does Karana make for Tutok?
9. How do Karana and Tutok spend their time together?
10. How does Karana feel when the Aleuts finally leave?
11. Who is Mon-a-nee?
12. Why does Karana look for stones the same color as the stones in the necklace Tutok gave her?

Chapters 24-29:
1. Karana imagines her sister smiling at Karana's children "...so different from the ones I always wished to have..." What "children" does Karana have?
2. Why does Karana call Mon-a-nee (a male), a "mother"?
3. Karana stops killing most animals. Which ones? Why?
4. How does Karana keep track of time, at first? Why does she stop?
5. How does Rontu die? How does Karana end up with his son?
6. What is the earthquake like? How does it make Karana feel? How does it make her life harder?
7. How does Karana react when she sees a ship unlike the Aleut boat? Why don't the men find her?
8. How long is it before another boat comes?
9. Why has the boat come? What does Karana do when the men ask where the otters are?
10. How do the men treat Karana?
11. How do you imagine her to look as the ship takes her away? Which of her "friends" and possessions does she have with her?

Author's Note
1. How old was Karana when she was found? What was the year?
2. Why does the author refer to Karana as a "girl Robinson Crusoe" (p. 187)?
3. Who befriended her after her rescue?
4. How did she communicate?
5. Was Karana reunited with the other Indians of Ghalas-at?
6. Where is she buried?
7. What is the Island of the Blue Dolphins called now? What is it like today?

Aleut 9	cormorants 10	kelp 11	mesa 12
ravine 12	intruders 12	toyon 12	parley 13
leagues 15	clattered 15	reefs 16	befell 18
sparingly 19	carcasses 23	pelt 23	

Directions: Divide the words among the members of your group. Turn to the pages on which your words appear in the novel. After looking at how each word is used, complete a word map for each of your words and share them with the rest of the group.

Synonyms

_____

_____

_____

_____

Drawing or Symbol to Help You Remember the Word's Meaning

WORD:

Definition in Your Own Words:

_____

_____

_____

_____

Word Used in a Sentence:

_____

_____

_____

_____

_____

_____

_____

snared 33	shirker 33	portioned 33	abalone 33
decreed 34	shrouded 37	awl 42	beckoned 43
howling 45	forlorn 46	scurrying 48	snarling 48
slunk 48	lair 49	switch 51	sandspit 52

Directions: Form a group of three. Cut out the sets below. Mix them up and put them face down on the table in the middle. Take turns picking cards and reading the clues aloud. Together, figure out the mystery words. Look at the vocabulary list above if you need to. (Each person in the group should be able to match the cards and words by the time you are finished.)

Set #1:

This word comes from a Spanish word.	A synonym for this noun is "sea ear."	The flesh is used for food and the shell is used for ornament.

Set #2:

A cougar might rest here.	This noun has one syllable.	A wild dog has one, but a pet dog doesn't.

Set #3:

The homophone for this word means "sum total."	You might use one to make an extra hole in your belt.	A furniture-maker might have one.

Set #4:

This word has several meanings; it can be a noun or a verb.	You could use nettles or an apple-tree branch to make one.	Some schoolmasters used them to whip their students.

Set #5:

This noun is a compound word.	It does NOT mean to project gritty granules from your mouth.	It would be at the beach, but not on a mountaintop.

Set #6:

It is NOT a compliment to be called one.	If you work hard, you are NOT one.	This word comes from the word "shark."

Set #7:

An antonym for this word is "merry."	A synonym for this word is "desolate."	This word rhymes with a yellow vegetable.

Set #8:

This word has two syllables.	This might be done to money or chores.	This word comes from the Latin one for "share."

Set #9:

The root word can be a noun or verb.	A synonym for this word is "trapped."	This might be done to a grouse or rabbit.

headland 57	stunted 57	smother 61
crevices 63	omen 73	brackish 78

Use the letters and pictures to figure out the words. Then try creating some of your own from vocabulary words in previous lists and have a partner solve.

1.   (- **AYONS**)   +   **EVICES**   = _____

2. **S** +   = _____

3. **ST**   +[- **G**]   + **TED** = _____

4. **H** + [ - **B**] + **L** + [- **H**] = _____

5. **BR** + [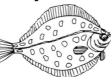 -**s**] + [ - **f**] = _____

6. **O** +    = _____

Write the word that goes with each definition.
1. dwarfed, having had its growth slowed down   _____
2. land sticking out into the water   _____
3. sign that something is going to happen   _____
4. cracks, grooves   _____
5. water that is a mixture of fresh and salty   _____
6. suffocate   _____

| pitch 84 | gruel 84 | tusklike 86 | waddling 88 |
| pursuer 91 | flank 92 | lobe 94 | matted 102 |

Directions: One partner is responsible for unscrambling each list word and drawing a line to its definition. The other partner is responsible for including each word in a sentence.

Scrambled list words	Unscrambled words	Definitions
1. usurper	_____	a. tar
2. atdemt	_____	b. walking with short, rocking steps
3. bole	_____	c. one who chases
4. stikluke	_____	d. side of animal between ribs and hip
5. cipth	_____	e. similar to the two long teeth of an elephant
6. legur	_____	f. tangled
7. fankl	_____	g. thin cereal
8. agdilbwud	_____	h. round part

Sentences

1. _____
2. _____
3. _____
4. _____
5. _____
6. _____
7. _____
8. _____

sea caves 108	devilfish 110	muzzles 115	haunches 115
lupines 119	prey 123	sinew 125	leeches 130

Directions:
1. With a partner, put each of the list words in one of the boxes below.

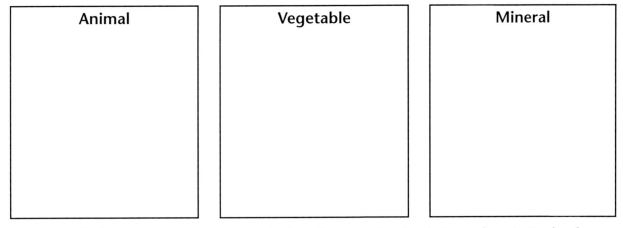

Animal	Vegetable	Mineral

2. With the same partner, research the plants and animals in each pair. Each of you can find information and interesting facts about one in each pair; then complete the charts together.

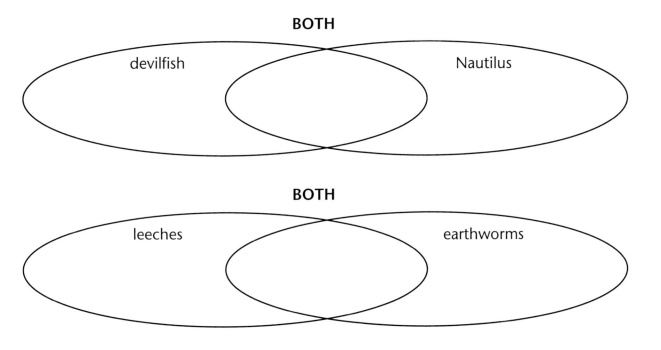

BOTH

devilfish   Nautilus

BOTH

leeches   earthworms

Directions: Members of a small group should brainstorm as many synonyms as they can for each **boldfaced** word and add to the synonym trains begun below. After thinking of all you can on your own, use the dictionary and thesaurus to find more synonyms. You can also add related words such as antonyms, but label them.

1. **oblong**—oval—

2. **slung**—tossed—

3. **peered**—gazed—

4. **circlet**—ring—

5. **prow**—front—

6. **reproachfully**—rebukingly—

swoop 157	fledglings 157	hobble 158	quiver 162
snares 166	toluache weed 167	thong 168	wreckage 176
galleons 187	excavations 188		

Directions: Use words from the vocabulary box to complete the analogies, below. Using the analogies as models, create analogies for five more of the vocabulary words and exchange with a partner.

Samples: NO is to YES as OFF is to ON. *(Both pairs are opposites.)*
HILL is to MOUNTAIN as STREAM is to RIVER. *(Both pairs are similar, but a hill is smaller than a mountain and a stream is smaller than a river.)*

1. LAMBS are to SHEEP as _____ are to BIRDS.

2. DOWN is to UP as _____ is to ASCEND.

3. HOLSTER is to GUN as _____ is to ARROWS.

4. DIRIGIBLES are to AIRCRAFT as _____ are to SHIPS.

5. LASSO is to ROPE as _____ is to LEATHER.

6. _____ is to _____ as _____ is to _____.

7. _____ is to _____ as _____ is to _____.

8. _____ is to _____ as _____ is to _____.

9. _____ is to _____ as _____ is to _____.

10. _____ is to _____ as _____ is to _____.

Directions: Fill in the chart with words that tell about Karana.

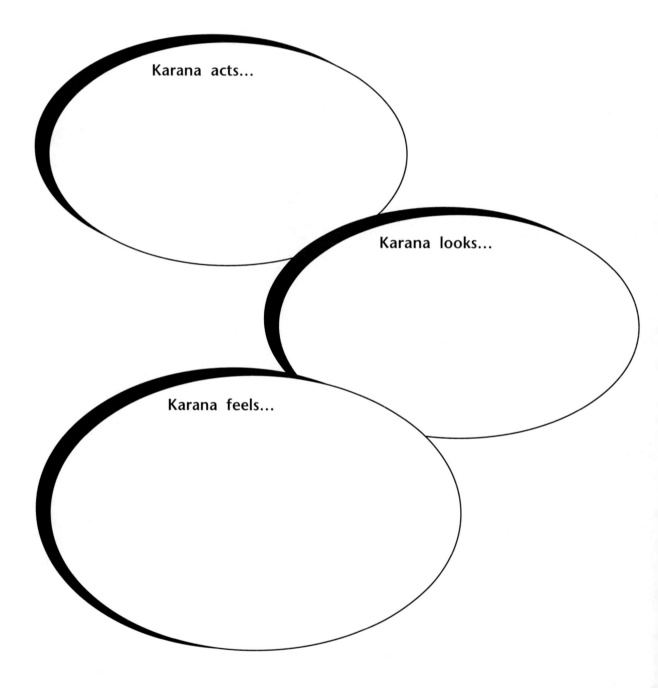

Karana acts...

Karana looks...

Karana feels...

Directions:

1. Calculate how far Karana's home is from Santa Barbara, in miles.
    (Captain Orlov mentions that it is 20 leagues from the island to the coast at Santa Barbara.)

2. Label Los Angeles.

3. According to the Author's Note, San Nicolas (the Island of the Blue Dolphins) is the outermost of the eight Channel Islands, 75 miles southwest of Los Angeles. Label the Channel Islands on the map below.

4. Karana spent the later years of her life at the Santa Barbara Mission, where she is now buried. Label Santa Barbara.

5. Captain Orlov and the Aleuts came from the Aleutian Islands. Draw an arrow pointing in the correct direction, and label it "to the Aleutian Islands."

Scale

0   40   80   120 160

California

Directions: Talk with other members of your group about how Karana turned her loneliness, boredom, and fear into strength.

Now think about your own life. When have you been alone—or at least on your own, in some way? Were you lonely? If so, what helped you feel better? Did some good come out of those times of solitude? What did you learn about yourself? Write your thoughts and feelings below.

_____

_____

_____

_____

_____

_____

_____

_____

_____

_____

_____

By _____

Name_____

Directions: Complete the Venn diagram by supplying words or phrases that describe Karana and words or phrases that describe Tutok. Descriptors that apply to both girls go in the middle, overlapping area.

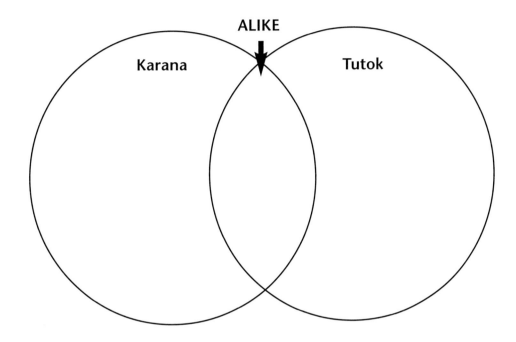

Using the information in the Venn diagram, write a paragraph in which you compare and contrast the two girls. You may use the framework, below, if you wish.

Karana and Tutok found that they had much in common. Both of them _____

_____. Also, they

_____.

On the other hand, _____

_____

_____

_____.

Directions: At first Karana tried to keep herself hidden from Tutok. She was worried that if Tutok found her, the adult Aleuts might learn where she was, too. What if Tutok had told the adults and they had discovered Karana? Write the scene the way it might have happened.

Pre-Writing: Take a few minutes to relax and imagine the scene as Karana watches the Aleut fires and considers the different places she might go. Follow her as she heads back to the cave. What do you see as she passes the shelter she built? What has happened to the whale-bone fence she put up around it? Back in the cave, can you smell the aroma of the fish she burns for light? What other smells do you notice? Follow her again as she leaves the safety of the cave with her half-finished skirt in her hand. Where is she going? Why? Watch as she stops her work to hold the skirt up to her waist. Notice that Rontu has leaped to his feet. There is Tutok...and whom do you see behind her? What expressions do the Aleuts have on their faces? What do they say? How does Karana react?......Let the happenings flow in your mind until you realize how the story is taking shape.......Then return to the here and now, pick up your pen, and jot down some notes.

Writing: Write the scene, in narrative or dialogue form.

Post-Writing: Read the scene to your group. Discuss with the other members of your group how Karana's thoughts could be altered to sound more natural, more in character—and what details might be added to the Aleut's actions to make the episode more vivid.

Directions: During her time alone on the island, Karana had to make many decisions. In each case, below, list as many "pros" and "cons" as you can for each choice. Then select one decision and write a paragraph in which you explain why you feel that Karana did or did not make the best choice.

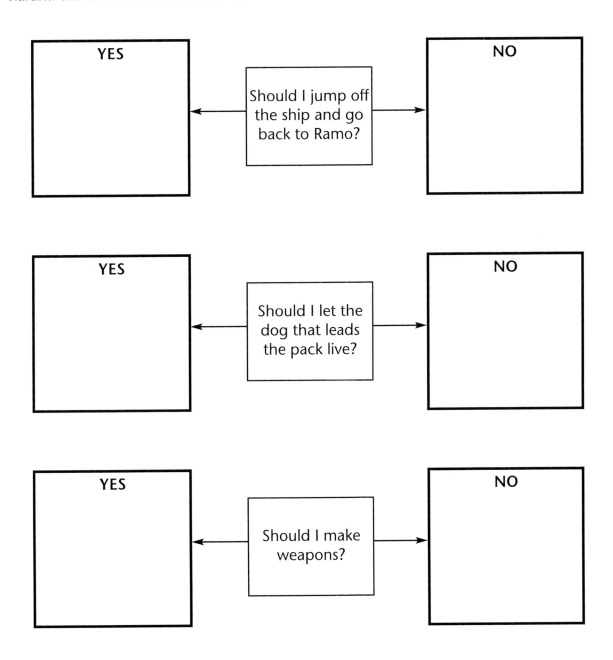

YES / Should I jump off the ship and go back to Ramo? / NO

YES / Should I let the dog that leads the pack live? / NO

YES / Should I make weapons? / NO

Directions: Write down what you learn from your reading about the animals listed on the chart. Then use reference books from your library to find out more about one of the animals listed. At the bottom of the page, write a paragraph about that animal.

Animal	Appearance	Behavior	Usefulness to Humans	Dangerous to Humans?
elephant seal				
otter				
octopus				
cormorant				
fox				
dolphin				

For my research, I chose the _____.

Name_____

Directions: Karana had to deal with her feelings of loss after several deaths. Pretend that you are Karana and write memorial poems for your father, your brother, and your dog.

Prewriting: Jot down what you remember about each. What did they look like? How did they act? What good times did you share? How did knowing each one change you? What do you miss, now that they're gone?

Mid Writing: Experiment with line breaks in different places. Eliminate words you don't need. Choose your favorite memorial poem and write it in the frame provided below.

Post-Writing: Read your poems aloud. Ask others in your group to comment on them.

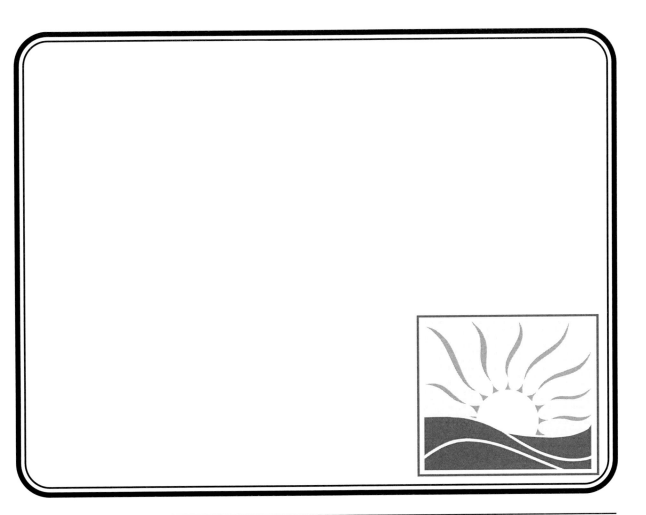

Directions: Authors sometimes use **figurative language** to make descriptions more vivid for readers. **Similes** are comparisons using the words "like" or "as." For example: "Her fingers were *like* icicles."

Below are several examples of figurative language used by Scott O'Dell in *Island of the Blue Dolphins*.

    a) Analyze each by telling what two things are being compared, and how they are alike.

    b) Write your own simile to suggest a similar quality, in a different way.

1.   "In the morning when he crawls out of his tent he sits on a rock and combs until the beard shines like a cormorant's wing," Ramo said.

    a. _____ is like _____ because both _____

    _____.

    b. ...until the beard shines like _____

2.   "I have never seen the ocean so calm and the sky looks like a blue shell."

    a. _____ is like _____ because both _____

    _____.

    b. ...the sky looks like _____

3.   "...the sun [was] so hot that the sea was like a sun itself."

    a. _____ is like _____ because both _____

    _____.

    b. ...the sea was like _____

Name_____

Crossword Puzzle

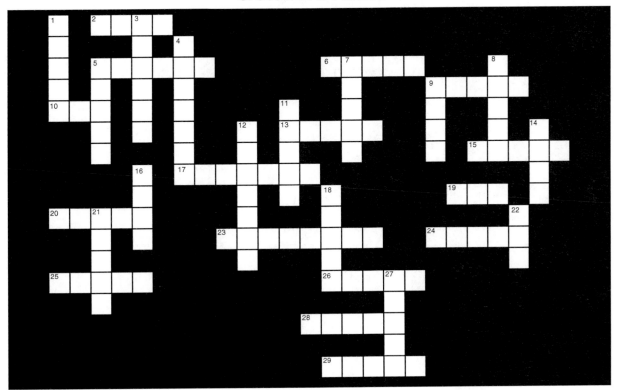

ACROSS

2. Karana smoothed out shelves in the rock so they wouldn't get her food.
5. Karana heated these and dropped them in water to cook seeds.
6. Karana's yellow-eyed enemy, then friend.
9. The _____fish left a trail of ink.
10. The little fish used for light were sai-____.
13. She gave Karana a necklace.
15. Karana used this from seals to bind poles together for her house.
17. The cave was an additional one.
19. Female sea elephants were killed for____.
20. Karana covered the embers with these.
23. Number of years Karana is alone.
24. Karana used _____ ribs for a fence.
25. This kind of wave crashed over the island.
26. Karana needed the sea elephant's tooth to make one.
28. Karana's older sister
29. furs

DOWN

1. Tainor and Lurai
3. the chief who is killed
4. Women were not allowed to make these.
5. Karana makes one of cormorant feathers.
7. He tried to cheat the island people.
8. He was Chief after #3 Down.
9. Karana killed many of the wild ones.
11. The Aleuts come to hunt these.
12. The island is shaped like one.
14. Otter lie in beds of this.
16. Karana's people refuse to share the white____ with the Aleuts.
18. Karana wove baskets from these.
21. The Aleuts promise beads and spear_____.
22. color of abalone flesh
27. The first ship Karana ever sees is one.

Name_____

Directions: Label each statement "T" for True or "F" for False.

____ 1. The story is told by Karana.

____ 2. The events in the story took place during the 1600s.

____ 3. The Aleuts planned to make slaves of the islanders.

____ 4. Captain Orlov killed Karana's father.

____ 5. Kimki became the new leader after Chief Chowig died.

____ 6. Karana decided to stay on the island because her father's body was there.

____ 7. The wild dogs killed Karana's brother.

____ 8. Karana hesitated to make weapons because women on the island were forbidden to make them.

____ 9. Lightning started a fire that destroyed Ghalas-at.

____ 10. Karana built her house near the old village.

____ 11. Karana's people sometimes killed female sea elephants for their oil.

____ 12. Karana tried to leave the island by canoe, but returned when the boat leaked.

____ 13. Karana used bamboo for a fence around her shelter.

____ 14. Karana made utensils from stones.

____ 15. Karana cooked seeds and roots by roasting them on a stick.

____ 16. Karana used the bodies of small dried insects for light.

____ 17. Karana wanted to kill a sea elephant so that she could use the teeth for a spear.

____ 18. The sea elephant injured Karana by gashing her arm.

____ 19. Karana was able to make spear points from teeth because she captured the sea elephant with a net.

____ 20. Karana named the dog after her brother.

Name_____

Directions: Fill in each blank with a word or phrase.

1. The narrator of *Island of the Blue Dolphins* is _____.

2. The events in the story took place during the __00s

3. The Aleuts came to the island to hunt _____.

4. Karana's father was killed by _____.

5. Kimki became the new _____ after Karana's father died.

6. Karana left the rescue ship because her _____ was still on the island.

7. Wild _____ killed Ramo.

8. On Ghalas-at, _____ were not allowed to make weapons.

9. Karana could hear the voices and see the shapes of the dead in the houses, so she made _____ in all of them.

10. Karana decided not to build her house near the old _____ because of the memories and the sand.

11. Karana's people sometimes killed female sea elephants for their _____.

12. When Karana left the island, she might have kept on going if the canoe hadn't _____.

13. Karana used _____ for a fence around her shelter.

14. Karana made utensils from _____ for cooking fish.

15. Karana made gruel by heating stones and dropping them into _____ of water containing seeds and roots.

16. Karana used the bodies of small dried _____ for light.

17. Karana wanted to kill a _____so that she could use the teeth for a spear.

18. Karana hurt herself by _____ while fleeing the male sea elephant.

19. Karana got the teeth she needed after the old bull sea elephant was killed by _____.

20. Karana named the dog Rontu because _____.

Identification: Find a character on the right who matches the description on the left. Write the letter of the character next to the matching number. Each character is to be used only once.

___ 1. Karana's dog
___ 2. Karana's brother
___ 3. Karana's father
___ 4. leader of the Aleuts
___ 5. Karana's Aleut friend
___ 6. Karana's sister
___ 7. the new chief after Chief Chowig
___ 8. Karana's female bird
___ 9. Karana's male bird
___ 10. A young otter saved by Karana
___ 11. the narrator

a. Kimki
b. Chief Chowig
c. Rontu
d. Mon-a-nee
e. Tutok
f. Ulape
g. Ramo
h. Lurai
i. Captain Orlov
j. Tainor
k. Karana

Directions: Write the letter of the BEST answer.

1. Karana was taken away from the island in
   A. 1153
   B. 1353
   C. 1653
   D. 1853

2. The Island of the Blue Dolphins is located
   A. near the Alaskan peninsula
   B. off the coast of Southern California
   C. near the Hawaiian mainland
   D. off the coast of Indonesia

3. Captain Orlov came to hunt for
   A. otter
   B. dolphins
   C. abalone
   D. cormorants

4. The Aleuts and the islanders fought because the Aleuts broke the agreement to
    A. leave before the summer was over
    B. share their fish
    C. leave the animals on the island alone
    D. pay for the pelts

5. Kimki becomes the new chief because
    A. the villagers no longer trust Chief Chowig
    B. Karana's father has been killed
    C. every winter a new chief is chosen
    D. Chief Chowig left for help and never returned

6. The women in the village start doing "men's work" because
    A. the men refuse to do it
    B. few men are left alive to do it
    C. the women are demanding equal rights
    D. they see the Aleut women hunting

7. The islanders leave the Island of the Blue Dolphins because
    A. they are afraid the Aleuts will return and attack
    B. there is no food left
    C. there are no more otters to hunt
    D. the Aleuts threaten to kill them if they don't leave

8. Karana stays behind on the island because she is
    A. afraid of the storm
    B. afraid of the ship
    C. loyal to her brother
    D. loyal to her father

9. Ramo dies from
    A. hunger
    B. thirst
    C. disease
    D. injuries

10. Karana uses whale ribs to make
    A. a ladder
    B. a fence
    C. necklaces
    D. spears

11. Karana sets out in a canoe hoping to find
    A. the island to the West where the dolphins live
    B. the place the voices of the dead told her to find
    C. the islands the Aleuts had come from
    D. the country to the east which Kimki had described

12. Which of the following DOESN'T Karana eat?
    A. fish
    B. otter
    C. seeds
    D. roots

13. When Rontu dies, Karana's reaction is most like which of the following?
    A. the irritation of an employer who finds that his hardest-working employee
       has quit
    B. the grief of a person who finds that an old friend is dead
    C. the anger of a soldier who follows orders to kill against his will
    D. the pride of a bullfighter who finally succeeds in killing the bull

14. Which of the following best explains why Tutok gave presents to Karana?
    A. Tutok's parents told Tutok to be kind to the lonely girl.
    B. Tutok wanted Karana to be her friend.
    C. Tutok hoped that Karana would give her a cormorant skirt.
    D. Tutok wanted Karana to give the dog back.

15. How long had Karana been alone on the island before she was taken to the
    mission?
    A. 6 months
    B. 2 years
    C. 18 years
    D. 28 years

Essay

Directions: Choose A or B and circle the letter of the question you decide to answer. Answer the question in one paragraph. Include at least three examples or reasons for your answers.

A. Karana's feelings toward animals change during the time she lives alone on the island. Explain how. Mention at least three animals.

B. Karana is able to survive because of the skills she learns. Describe at least three of these skills and explain how they keep her alive.

Identification: Find the description on the right that matches the character name on the left. Write the letter of the description next to the matching number. Each character is to be used only once.

_____ 1.   Kimki

_____ 2.   Chief Chowig

_____ 3.   Rontu

_____ 4.   Mon-a-nee

_____ 5.   Tutok

_____ 6.   Ulape

_____ 7.   Ramo

_____ 8.   Lurai

_____ 9.   Captain Orlov

_____ 10.   Tainor

_____ 11.   Karana

a. Karana made her a circlet of shells.

b. "Fox Eyes;" the yellow-eyed leader of the dogs

c. She packed two boxes of earrings and marked herself "unmarried" with blue clay.

d. He was six years old and quick as a cricket.

e. Wounded by the Aleuts, this young otter was nursed back to health.

f. He warned the villagers that the Aleuts did not understand friendship.

g. the "dishonest Russian" who promised beads and a spearhead for every pelt

h. He was the male bird whose wings Karana clipped.

i. Two of her speckled eggs hatched.

j. He told the women they would have to do dangerous men's work now that many of the men were dead.

k. secret name for "Girl with the Long Black Hair"

Short Answer

Directions: Answer each question in one or two sentences.

1. What is the setting (approximate time and place) of the story?

2. What were Captain Orlov's motives in coming to the island?

3. How had past experience shown Chief Chowig that the Aleuts were not to be trusted?

4. What do you think would have happened if the islanders had not confronted and fought the Aleuts?

5. During WWI and WWII, women took factory jobs that had formerly been considered "men's work." Explain how something like this happened in *Island of the Blue Dolphins.*

6. Why did the islanders leave the island and what happened to them?

7. Why did Karana plan to kill the wild dogs someday?

8. What is our word for "devilfish" and why did Karana try to kill one?

9. Why did Karana abandon her plan to leave the island by canoe?

10. How did Karana solve the problem of need for shelter?

11. How did Karana solve the problem of need for food?

12. How did Karana solve the problem of how to make a fire?

13. How did Karana's feelings about Tutok change and why?

14. Why did Karana decide never again to kill cormorants, otters, seals, and other animals?

15. About how long was Karana alone on the island and how did she get off?

Essay

Directions: Select A or B and circle the letter of the question you decide to answer.

A. When the ship finally arrives at the end, Karana has some mixed feelings. Write a series of sentences that show what she is thinking and feeling inside and what she is remembering and wondering as she sails away from the island.

B. "Courage is the thing! All goes if courage goes."

Explain whether or not Karana's response to hardship supports the quote by Sir J.M. Barrie, above. (How did Karana display courage? Was it courage—or something else—that helped her survive?)

Answer Key

Activity #1: Answers to the Anticipation Guide will vary, but students should be able to give reasons.

Activity #2: Ratings will vary; point out that thirst is usually #1 in a survival situation (where freezing to death is not a consideration) because you can go longer without food than water.

Study Questions
Chapters 1-4:
1. Karana, a Pacific Islander with long dark hair—adult now, about 12 when the story begins. As a storyteller, she is objective and direct, a close observer of people and nature. 2. On the Island of the Blue Dolphins (village of Ghalas-at) about 30 miles off the California coast. 3. Aleuts have come to hunt otter for pelts. 4. Ulape is Karana's older sister and Ramo is her younger brother. 5. Karana's father, chief on the island. It is customary to keep one's real name secret so that its protective magic does not wear off. 6. They exploited the islanders by making them do all the hunting for otter. 7. It is dolphin-shaped and dolphins are sometimes seen nearby. 8. white bass they catch 9. one string of beads and one spearhead for each pelt; They stay a couple of weeks or so. 10. The two sides fight and many of the island's men are killed or injured.

Chapters 5-8:
1. 27 are killed; 15 remain (7 old men). 2. the old man who takes over as chief after Chief Chowig is killed 3. Women do more dangerous "men's" work of hunting fish and birds. Men resent the switch and soon women are harvesting and men hunting, again. 4. Karana describes the "sickness" that the memory of the dead brought over the survivors. 5. Kimki heads toward the East to a country where he had been as a boy, hoping to make a place for his people there. He never returns, but he sends the white men to get his people. 6. Karana packs needles, an awl, a knife, cooking pots and a box with earrings. 7. If they wait, the ship will be driven on the rocks. 8. She goes back to be with her brother, mistakenly left behind on the island. 9. He goes off to get a canoe and is attacked by wild dogs.

Chapters 9-11:
1. She burns the houses because she cannot stand the memories of those who are dead or gone. 2. She sleeps on a rock during the warm weather, builds a temporary shelter of brush on the side of a hill near a stream. 3. It is forbidden for women to make weapons, but she needs them to defend against the dogs, to catch fish, etc. 4. She is looking for spearheads. She finds only beads (although Captain Orlov had promised spearheads as well). 5. She uses sea elephant teeth for spearheads; wood, stone, and feathers for bow and arrows. 6. She eats fish, shellfish, seeds, roots, birds.

7. depressed; chances that the white man will rescue her during the winter are slim.
8. She hopes to find the land to the East described by Kimki. Her boat leaks and she lets the dolphins lead her home. 9. She builds a house of tree-poles bound with sinew and covered with kelp (on the side of a hill near a stream, with a view of the ocean).

Chapters 12-15:
1. a fence around her shelter to keep out the dogs; She might have used wood, but the dogs could have gnawed through. 2. At the beginning of the world, these two gods quarreled about whether or not people had to die; Tumaiyowit went to another world under this one, so people die because he did. 3. by hollowing out stones with sand 4. She drops hot rocks into water-filled baskets. 5. When burned, they give off light. 6. for its teeth (spearpoints) 7. running from a sea elephant, who is fighting with another sea elephant 8. Injured, he lies still and she hesitates, figuring he will die. 9. The old sea elephant dies in the battle with the younger one. 10. Rontu—because he has the eyes of a fox.

Chapters 16-19:
1. She makes the canoe smaller so that she can lift it. 2. There she is safe from the dogs. 3. a devilfish (octopus); They taste delicious. 4. He goes to confront the other dogs vying for leadership; he fights them and returns to Karana while the pack divides into two packs. 5. She clips the wings of two colorful birds nesting near her house. 6. She makes a skirt of yucca, a belt of sealskin, sandals of sealskin, flowers and whalebone pins for her hair. 7. The devilfish almost kills Rontu and exhausts her. She probably decides the trouble is not worth the effort.

Chapters 20-23:
1. She ties abalone shells on poles and the reflected light keeps the gulls away.
2. She is making a skirt of their feathers. 3. She sees effigies, bones of her ancestors; frightened. 4. About 14; she packed things that she would take to the cave in the ravine—two birds, skirt, stone utensils, beads, feathers, baskets, and weapons. 5. The men are off hunting, but she is afraid that the girl will discover her hiding place. 6. The girl is friendly, admiring Karana's skirt. Karana doesn't trust Tutok completely. 7. a bead necklace 8. a circlet of shells for her hair 9. naming themselves and surrounding objects, each in her own language 10. relieved that they are gone, but she misses Tutok 11. An otter injured by the hunters, nursed back to health by Karana, who becomes Karana's friend. 12. She wants to make matching earrings.

Chapters 24-29:
1. She has befriended several animals—a hurt gull, Mon-a-nee, the two birds and their fledglings, Rontu. 2. He returns with two baby otter; it seems that the mother must be gone, for he has taken over the maternal role. 3. Having befriended many, she decides that they are as important as people. 4. She keeps track of moons; cut a mark in door

pole, by counting winters. **5.** He dies, apparently of old age. After disappearing for a while, he is found by Karana; walks to her side and falls dead at her feet. Karana finds the pup that looks like him and drugs the pool at which he drinks with toluache weed. **6.** The earthquake doesn't do much damage, but it is accompanied by a tidal wave. Resolute, she simply starts undoing the damage. (The water has taken her food, weapons, canoe.) **7.** She is torn, worried that the ship might bring hunters, thinking of the life she has made for herself, but wanting to be where others live; by the time she hides, then dresses, they have headed off. **8.** about two years **9.** to hunt; She pretends she doesn't know what they mean. **10.** kindly, but patronizingly (having clothes made at once for her). **11.** proud, wearing her new blue dress, with her baskets at her side, her birds, and Rontu-Aru.

Author's Note:
1. about 30—1853 2. She survived by her own wits and skills on a "desert island," like the hero of the novel by Defoe. **3.** Father Gonzales at the Santa Barbara Mission **4.** in signs **5.** No, they had disappeared. **6.** on a hill near the Santa Barbara Mission **7.** San Nicolas; it's a secret U.S. Navy base and may someday be reclaimed by the sea.

Activity #3: Individual word maps will vary. Here are synonyms/definitions: *Aleut*—individual from the Aleutian Islands off Alaskan mainland; *cormorants*—sea birds; *kelp*—sea weed; *mesa*—land formation with flat top and steep walls; *ravine*—canyon, deep ditch; *intruders*—people who barge in but don't belong; *toyon*—type of bush; *parley*—talk; *leagues*—about 3 miles; *clattered*—made rattling noises; *reefs*—sandbanks, shoals; *befell*—happened to; *sparingly*—thriftily; *carcasses*—dead bodies; *pelt*—fur, skin

Activity #4: Sets: 1-abalone, 2-lair, 3-awl, 4-switch, 5-sandspit, 6-shirker, 7-forlorn, 8-portioned, 9-snared

Activity #5: Rebuses: 1-crevices, 2-smother, 3-stunted, 4-headland, 5-brackish, 6-omen; Definitions: 1-stunted 2-headland 3-omen 4-crevices 5-brackish 6-smother

Activity #6: 1. pursuer-c; 2. matted-f; 3. lobe-h; 4. tusklike-e; 5. pitch-a; 6. gruel-g; 7. flank-d; 8. waddling-b. Sentences will vary.

Activity #7: Animal—devilfish, muzzles, haunches, prey, sinew, leeches; Vegetable-lupine; Mineral-sea cave. Venn diagrams will vary.

Activity #8: Synonyms will vary.

Activity #9: 1-FLEDGLINGS; 2-SWOOP; 3-QUIVER; 4-GALLEONS; 5-THONG 6-10 will vary

Activity #10: Karana has long dark hair, "mothers" her younger brother, likes pretty clothing and flowers in her hair, quickly learns how to survive on her own, feels lonely but overcomes her loneliness, makes friends with animals

Activity #11:

1. 20 leagues = 20 x 3 miles =
   60 miles
2. through 5. see map at right

Activities #12-#17: are open-ended activities; there are no specific answers.

Activity #18: 1-beard is like a cormorant's wing; both shine; 2-sky is like a shell; both are blue; 3-sea is like sun; both are hot and bright.

to the Aleutian Islands

Santa Barbara
Los Angeles
Channel Islands

Activity #19:

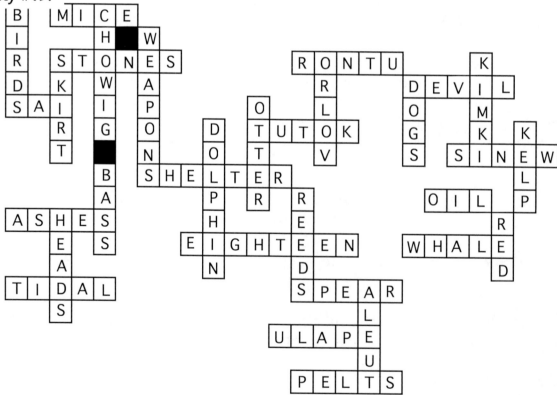

Comprehension Quiz, Regular Level
1-T; 2-F; 3-F; 4-T; 5-T; 6-F; 7-T; 8-T; 9-F; 10-F; 11-T; 12-T; 13-F; 14-T; 15-F; 16-F; 17-T; 18-F; 19-F; 20-F

Comprehension Quiz, Honors Level

1-Karana; 2-18; 3-otter; 4-Captain Orlov-Aleuts; 5-chief; 6-brother; 7-dogs; 8-women; 9-fires; 10-village; 11-oil; 12-leaked; 13-whale ribs; 14-stones; 15-baskets; 16-fish; 17-sea elephant; 18-falling; 19-a younger bull; 20-he had yellow eyes like a fox.

Unit Test, Regular Level

Identification: 1-c; 2-g; 3-b; 4-i; 5-e; 6-f; 7-a; 8-h; 9-j; 10-d; 11-k

Multiple Choice

1-D; 2-B; 3-A; 4-D; 5-B; 6-B; 7-A; 8-C; 9-D; 10-B; 11-D; 12-B; 13-B; 14-B; 15-C

Essay: Students who choose A should mention that Karana decides not to kill animals who are her friends—or might become friends. She has befriended an otter, a wild dog, birds. Students who choose B might mention that she learned to make a spear (which helped her get food), to make a house out of wood and sinew (which provided her with shelter), and to make a fire (which kept her warm and allowed her to cook).

Unit Test, Honors Level

Identification: 1-j; 2-f; 3-b; 4-e; 5-a; 6-c; 7-d; 8-i; 9-g; 10-h; 11-k

Short Answer:

1. The story takes place on an island off the coast of Southern California during the early-mid 1800s. 2. Orlov and the Aleuts had come to hunt otter. 3. In the past, Aleuts had forced the islanders to do the hunting for them. 4. The Aleuts probably would have left without paying them—and might have attacked them another time. 5. After many of the men on the island were killed by the Aleuts, the women had to do "men's work" like hunting. 6. Afraid that the Aleuts would return and attack, the islanders left on a ship of whites sent by Kimki, but were never seen again. 7. She wanted revenge since the dogs had killed her brother. 8. Karana wanted an octopus because they are tasty. 9. She started out once, but her canoe leaked and she almost got lost. 10. She first built a house of sticks, then built one of tree-poles bound by sinew and covered with kelp. 11. She ate roots and berries and trapped fish, small birds. 12. She used fire probably left by her people, covering the embers each night to keep them from dying out. 13. Although she mistrusted Tutok at first, she became the Aleut's friend because she was lonely. 14. These animals had all become her friends. 15. She was alone for about 18 years and was taken off by a ship of white men who had come to hunt otters.

Essay

A. Answers might include some of her memories of the relatives who died on the island, the animal friends she made there, the many survival problems she solved, observations of the curious white men who have rescued her, and her hopes that she will see her people again.

B. Students who choose B might point out that Karana would have died if she had let her fears overcome her. Although she did not know how to make weapons, was threatened by wild dogs, had little available food—she found the courage to solve these problems and survive.

Notes